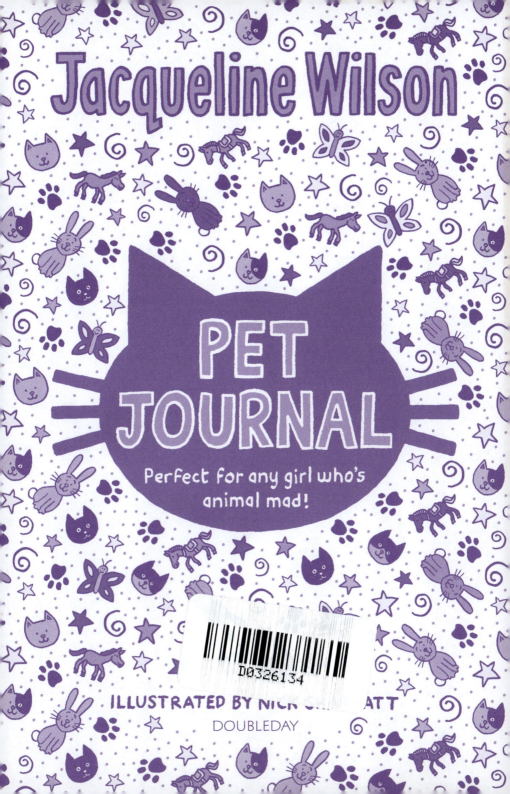

Jacqueline Wilson

PET JOURNAL

Perfect for any girl who's animal mad!

ILLUSTRATED BY NICK SHARRATT

DOUBLEDAY

I wonder if you've got a pet? If so, I'm sure they've become a very special part of your family. I don't think anything beats taking a bouncy little puppy for his first walk in the park, or curling up in an armchair with a soft, silky cat purring on your lap. Of course, having a pet is also a real responsibility. You have to learn to look after your pets properly and always treat them with love and care.

I totally adore my two cats. Jacob is grey and white and very beautiful. He's two-and-a-half now. Thomas was a little stray cat who came to live with me about a year ago. He's slinky and black with huge green eyes. Jacob and Thomas are great friends. They lick each other every morning, play hide-and-seek together all around the house, and sleep on my bed at night. I'm very touched that you send Jacob special messages and love him too.

Jacqueline Wilson

★ Your pet will also need special food to stay healthy and strong. And be careful that your pet doesn't accidentally eat something they shouldn't!

★ Your pet will need plenty of exercise — and if you have a dog or a pony, sometimes that might mean you'll need to go outside in the rain or even the snow!

★ One of the best things about having a pet is playing with them. You might want to buy your pet a special toy from a pet shop, but dogs love to chase after a tennis ball or a stick, and cats enjoy pouncing on tiny toy mice. Remember that if your pet is a little bit older, they might not want to play as much as a younger animal, so sometimes just a cuddle is the best thing.

★ There are lots of magazines and websites that you can read for more advice on animals, and how to look after your pet well.

★ If you're ever worried about your pet or think they might be poorly, tell a grown-up. Your pet might need a trip to the vet, who will be able to help. You can find out the address and phone number of your local vet, and write it down on the 'Important Addresses and Phone Numbers' page.

🐾 MY PETS 🐾

Every pet is different — yours might be soft and scruffy, sleek and beautiful, tiny and cuddly, big and boisterous! And every pet has a very different personality, different habits, and likes different things. What sort of pet do you have?

(If you don't have a pet yet, don't worry! Why not invent some imaginary pets here, like Marty in *The Worst Thing About My Sister*?)

My pet's name is _____

And he/she is a _____

His/her colour is _____

My pet is _____ years old.

He/she has been with my family for _____ months/years.

We got him/her from _____

My pet loves to eat _____

My pet sleeps _____

Games I like to play with my pet _____

My pet's personality is _____

Three words that best describe my pet _____

My favourite thing about my pet is _____

Why not stick a photo of your pet here — or draw a picture!

My pet's name is _____

And he/she is a _____

His/her colour is _____

My pet is _____ years old.

He/she has been with my family for _____ months/years.

We got him/her from _____

My pet loves to eat _____

My pet sleeps _____

Games I like to play with my pet _____

_____

My pet's personality is _____

_____

Three words that best describe my pet _____

_____

My favourite thing about my pet is _____

_____

Why not stick a photo of your pet here — or draw a picture!

My pet's name is _____

And he/she is a _____

His/her colour is _____

My pet is _____ years old.

He/she has been with my family for _____ months/years.

We got him/her from _____

My pet loves to eat _____

My pet sleeps _____

Games I like to play with my pet _____

_____

My pet's personality is _____

_____

Three words that best describe my pet _____

_____

My favourite thing about my pet is _____

_____

Why not stick a photo of your pet here — or draw a picture!

My pet's name is _____

And he/she is a _____

His/her colour is _____

My pet is _____ years old.

He/she has been with my family for _____ months/years.

We got him/her from _____

My pet loves to eat _____

My pet sleeps _____

Games I like to play with my pet _____

_____

My pet's personality is _____

_____

Three words that best describe my pet _____

_____

My favourite thing about my pet is _____

_____

Why not stick a photo of your pet here – or draw a picture!

☙ MY DREAM PET ☙

If you love animals, you might have thought about what your dream pet would be. Imagine you're allowed any pet in the whole world. What would you choose? A tiny golden puppy with big, dark eyes? A glossy, gleaming horse, like Black Beauty? Or what about something exotic and exciting like a fearsome tiger or a playful chimpanzee?

☙ UNUSUAL PETS ☙

Dogs, cats and rabbits are the most popular pets today –
but lots of people enjoy having some very unusual pets, too.
Have you ever thought about . . .

A TARANTULA? Some people find spiders really scary, but
others think a tarantula is a perfect pet! They are very quiet,
and easy to feed and care for. But most tarantulas don't like
to be handled, so if you want a pet that you can cuddle and
stroke a lot, this might not be the best choice for you.

A LIZARD? There are hundreds of different types of lizard,
and some make brilliant pets. A lizard is a big commitment,
just like a cat or dog – some can live to be over twenty
years old, and grow up to eight or even ten feet long!

A SNAKE? A snake might seem like quite a scary pet too,
but they are popular with lots of people. They are very hard
work, though – caring for a snake can be very expensive,
and many pet snakes like to try and escape from their
tanks when their owners are not looking!

A RAT? Rats are very intelligent, clean pets, who like lots
of sleep and lots of play! With care and attention they
can be very tame and friendly. They are very social animals,
so lots of people choose to have two pet rats together,
who can keep each other company.

Would you ever have an unusual pet?

_____

_____

_____

_____

🐾 CREATE A PET 🐾 SCRAPBOOK!

Having a pet can mean lots of fun experiences, and lots of brilliant memories! To help you make the most of your pet, why not keep a pet scrapbook? You can start it here, or find a blank notebook if you like. Collect together photographs and pictures of your pet, and any other mementos you can find — maybe a leaf from your dog's favourite spot in the park, or a piece of fabric from your cat's favourite blanket!

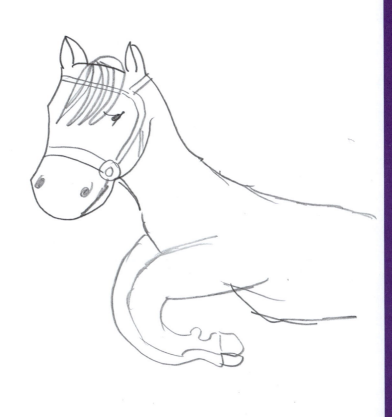

☙ USE YOUR ☙ IMAGINATION!

Have you ever wondered what your pet gets up to when you're not around? Maybe they just sleep, eat and behave themselves . . . but what if they secretly had all sorts of fun adventures? Imagine your family has gone out for the day and left your pet alone in the house. What sort of day do you think he or she would have?

_____

_____

_____

_____

_____

_____

_____

_____

_____

_____

_____

_____

_____

❀ PUZZLE TIME! ❀

❀ WORDSEARCH! ❀

There are ten words hidden, all related to pets. Good luck!

T	I	B	B	A	R	A	W	F
O	B	T	V	C	E	R	A	R
R	F	A	R	A	T	H	R	Y
T	A	A	R	O	S	G	M	T
O	I	E	I	U	M	K	E	H
I	H	C	D	T	A	S	P	G
S	C	B	E	I	H	A	O	U
E	V	G	W	W	A	F	I	A
C	U	D	D	L	Y	W	U	N
D	Y	P	A	Z	Q	J	E	L
V	M	O	X	L	A	Y	O	L

❀ LETTER CHALLENGE! ❀

How many words can you make from these letters?
Give yourself three minutes, and challenge your friends!

KINGCHARLESSPANIEL

Here are two to help you out:
Kiss Pink

❀ UNSCRAMBLE THESE WORDS ❀
TO REVEAL THE PET! ❀

1. Pingeaugi   **2.** Bitbar   **3.** Doople   **4.** Sipernatac
5. Troistoe   **6.** Shtamer

🐾 PET QUIZ 🐾

How well do you know pets in Jacqueline Wilson's books?
Find out here . . .

1. In THE WORST THING ABOUT MY SISTER,
Marty has six toy horses. Can you name them?

2. In CANDYFLOSS, Floss's little cat Lucky has
very beautiful eyes — what colour are they?

3. Without looking back at the first page of this Journal,
can you name both of Jacqueline's cats?

4. In COOKIE, Beauty would love a real rabbit, but her dad
buys her a giant toy rabbit instead. What does she name it?

5. In THE SUITCASE KID, Andy has a toy rabbit,
too — Radish. What kind of rabbit is he?

6. In BIG DAY OUT, Marty and Melissa visit a pet
show and fall in love with a cat named Anastasia.
What breed of cat is she?

7. When they eventually find a kitten of their own, which
famous rescue centre do they get him from?

8. In HETTY FEATHER, which glamorous character
owns six sleek horses?

✿ BRILLIANT PET ✿ FACTS!

Did you know . . . If you decide to get a tortoise as a pet, you might end up passing it on to your own children – and even to your grandchildren! Tortoises can live up to 150 years old! The oldest tortoise ever, Tui Malila, lived to be an amazing 188 years old.

Did you know . . . The smallest cat in the world was a tiny blue Himalayan-Persian called Tinker Toy. He lived in America and was just 7cm tall!

Did you know . . . The oldest dog in the world today is a terrier called Max, who lives in America. He's twenty-six years old! But the oldest dog ever was an Australian cattle dog named Bluey, who was twenty-nine.

Did you know . . . Several years ago, you could buy lots of amazing pets from Harrods, a huge shop in London – including lion cubs! Luckily, you can't do that today, as it's very important that wild animals like lions are able to grow up in their natural surroundings.

Did you know . . . The richest pet in the world is thought to be a German Shepherd called Gunter. When his owner died, she left her beloved dog all her money – around £90,000!

Did you know . . . The first animal to travel into space was a dog. Laika was a Russian stray, who was trained for her space mission along with two other dogs, Albina and Mushka. She was very brave, and very intelligent.

Did you know . . . Cats almost never purr at other cats. It's a sound that they usually make around people, instead of animals!

IMPORTANT ADDRESSES AND PHONE NUMBERS

Name: _____

Address: _____

_____

Phone Number: _____

Email: _____

Name: _____

Address: _____

_____

Phone Number: _____

Email: _____

Name: _____

Address: _____

_____

Phone Number: _____

Email: _____

Name: _____

Address: _____

_____

Phone Number: _____

Email: _____

JANUARY

Hee hee hee!

I'd have given anything for a proper pet, though not necessarily something fluffy. A real porcupine would be ultra-cool. Or a turtle who could live in the bath. Or a hyena that laughed at my jokes.

THE WORST THING ABOUT MY SISTER

1 JANUARY

2 JANUARY

3 JANUARY

4 JANUARY

5 JANUARY

6 JANUARY

7 JANUARY

8 JANUARY

9 JANUARY

10 JANUARY

11 JANUARY

12 JANUARY

13 JANUARY

14 JANUARY

15 JANUARY

16 JANUARY

17 JANUARY

18 JANUARY

19 JANUARY

20 JANUARY

21 JANUARY

22 JANUARY

23 JANUARY

24 JANUARY

25 JANUARY

26 JANUARY

27 JANUARY

28 JANUARY

29 JANUARY

30 JANUARY

31 JANUARY

NOTES

FEBRUARY

There's a rabbit called Lettuce at this home but it's a bit limp, like its name. It doesn't sit up and give you a friendly lick like a dog. I think I'd like a Rottweiler — and then all my enemies had better WATCH OUT.

THE STORY OF TRACY BEAKER

FEBRUARY

1 FEBRUARY

2 FEBRUARY

3 FEBRUARY

4 FEBRUARY

5 FEBRUARY

6 FEBRUARY

7 FEBRUARY

8 FEBRUARY

9 FEBRUARY

10 FEBRUARY

11 FEBRUARY

12 FEBRUARY

13 FEBRUARY

14 FEBRUARY

15 FEBRUARY

16 FEBRUARY

17 FEBRUARY

18 FEBRUARY

19 FEBRUARY

20 FEBRUARY

21 FEBRUARY

22 FEBRUARY

23 FEBRUARY

24 FEBRUARY

25 FEBRUARY

26 FEBRUARY

27 FEBRUARY

28 FEBRUARY

MARCH

The cat rubbed against me, nuzzling in and purring when I stroked the side of her neck. Her bones felt so tiny and delicate underneath her soft fur. 'I wonder if you belong to anyone, little cat?' I said. 'You haven't got a collar on, have you? You don't look as if you've been fed for days. Dad, if she's really a stray can we keep her?'

CANDYFLOSS

1 MARCH

2 MARCH

3 MARCH

4 MARCH

5 MARCH

6 MARCH

7 MARCH

8 MARCH

9 MARCH

10 MARCH

11 MARCH

12 MARCH

13 MARCH

14 MARCH

15 MARCH

16 MARCH

17 MARCH

18 MARCH

19 MARCH

20 MARCH

21 MARCH

22 MARCH

23 MARCH

24 MARCH

25 MARCH

26 MARCH

27 MARCH

28 MARCH

29 MARCH

30 MARCH

31 MARCH

NOTES

APRIL

We didn't have any pets at home. Mum wasn't very keen on the idea because she said they made a mess. Could she possibly object to one teeny weeny little rabbit who mostly lived in a hat?

THE WORST THING ABOUT MY SISTER

1 APRIL

2 APRIL

3 APRIL

4 APRIL

5 APRIL

6 APRIL

7 APRIL

8 APRIL

9 APRIL

1O APRIL

11 APRIL

12 APRIL

13 APRIL

14 APRIL

15 APRIL

16 APRIL

17 APRIL

18 APRIL

19 APRIL

20 APRIL

21 APRIL

22 APRIL

23 APRIL

24 APRIL

25 APRIL

---

26 APRIL

27 APRIL

28 APRIL

29 APRIL

30 APRIL

MAY

Radish wriggled excitedly in my hand. She could hardly
wait till I got her boat unpacked from my satchel.
She hopped on board and was soon sailing
across the lake.

THE SUITCASE KID

1 MAY

2 MAY

3 MAY

4 MAY

5 MAY

6 MAY

7 MAY

8 MAY

9 MAY

10 MAY

11 MAY

12 MAY

13 MAY

14 MAY

15 MAY

16 MAY

17 MAY

18 MAY

19 MAY

20 MAY

21 MAY

22 MAY

23 MAY

24 MAY

25 MAY

26 MAY

27 MAY

28 MAY

29 MAY

30 MAY

31 MAY

NOTES

JUNE

I drew our imaginary mansion. We had two real black
cats for luck lapping from little bowls in the kitchen,
two poodles curled up together in their dog basket,
while twin black ponies grazed in a paddock
beside our rose garden.

MY SISTER JODIE

1 JUNE

2 JUNE

3 JUNE

4 JUNE

5 JUNE

6 JUNE

7 JUNE

8 JUNE

9 JUNE

10 JUNE

11 JUNE

12 JUNE

13 JUNE

14 JUNE

15 JUNE

16 JUNE

17 JUNE

18 JUNE

19 JUNE

20 JUNE

21 JUNE

22 JUNE

23 JUNE

24 JUNE

25 JUNE

26 JUNE

27 JUNE

28 JUNE

29 JUNE

30 JUNE

JULY

I sat up straight as six sleek horses cantered into the ring.
I was used to Dobbin and Rowley, the great shire horses
in Father's care at the farm. These dancing, prancing
horses seemed an elvish breed, so small and dainty. Two
were spotted, two piebald and two grey, all with their
manes and tails flowing, long and silky.

HETTY FEATHER

1 JULY

2 JULY

3 JULY

4 JULY

5 JULY

6 JULY

7 JULY

8 JULY

9 JULY

10 JULY

11 JULY

12 JULY

13 JULY

14 JULY

15 JULY

16 JULY

Flea

17 JULY

18 JULY

19 JULY

20 JULY

21 JULY

22 JULY

23 JULY

24 JULY

25 JULY

26 JULY

27 JULY

28 JULY

29 JULY

30 JULY

31 JULY

NOTES

AUGUST

'Oh, how cool! I want a dog that can dance!'
I said. 'I could train it to do all sorts of tricks!'
We looked along aisle after aisle, and saw tiny
lapdogs and great big butch Rottweilers
and fabulous snowy white huskies.

BIG DAY OUT

AUGUST

1 AUGUST

2 AUGUST

3 AUGUST

4 AUGUST

Ha ha ha! Chortle chortle! Tee hee hee!

5 AUGUST

6 AUGUST

7 AUGUST

8 AUGUST

9 AUGUST

10 AUGUST

11 AUGUST

12 AUGUST

13 AUGUST

14 AUGUST

15 AUGUST

16 AUGUST

17 AUGUST

18 AUGUST

19 AUGUST

20 AUGUST

21 AUGUST

22 AUGUST

23 AUGUST

24 AUGUST

25 AUGUST

26 AUGUST

27 AUGUST

28 AUGUST

29 AUGUST

30 AUGUST

31 AUGUST

NOTES

SEPTEMBER

Sam gave Lily real cabbage leaves for her tea and,
guess what, a carrot cake with a candle,
almost exactly the same as the one I'd drawn!

COOKIE

1 SEPTEMBER

2 SEPTEMBER

3 SEPTEMBER

4 SEPTEMBER

5 SEPTEMBER

6 SEPTEMBER

SEPTEMBER

7 SEPTEMBER

8 SEPTEMBER

9 SEPTEMBER

1O SEPTEMBER

11 SEPTEMBER

12 SEPTEMBER

13 SEPTEMBER

14 SEPTEMBER

15 SEPTEMBER

16 SEPTEMBER

17 SEPTEMBER

18 SEPTEMBER

19 SEPTEMBER

20 SEPTEMBER

21 SEPTEMBER

22 SEPTEMBER

23 SEPTEMBER

24 SEPTEMBER

25 SEPTEMBER

26 SEPTEMBER

27 SEPTEMBER

28 SEPTEMBER

29 SEPTEMBER

30 SEPTEMBER

OCTOBER

'You just like cute and cuddly animals. I want a really exciting pet,' I said. My head felt like a Noah's Ark as animals of all shapes and sizes trumpeted and roared and whinnied in my mind.

BIG DAY OUT

1 OCTOBER

2 OCTOBER

3 OCTOBER

4 OCTOBER

5 OCTOBER

6 OCTOBER

7 OCTOBER

8 OCTOBER

9 OCTOBER

1O OCTOBER

11 OCTOBER

12 OCTOBER

13 OCTOBER

14 OCTOBER

15 OCTOBER

16 OCTOBER

17 OCTOBER

18 OCTOBER

19 OCTOBER

20 OCTOBER

21 OCTOBER

22 OCTOBER

23 OCTOBER

24 OCTOBER

25 OCTOBER

26 OCTOBER

27 OCTOBER

28 OCTOBER

29 OCTOBER

30 OCTOBER

OCTOBER

31 OCTOBER

NOTES

NOVEMBER

I had to put Lucky down to fill one little bowl
with cat food and another with water. I was worried
she'd try to scoot straight out of the back door but
she waited patiently, licking her lips at the smell
of the food. 'Eat up, little Lucky,' I said.

CANDYFLOSS

1 NOVEMBER

2 NOVEMBER

3 NOVEMBER

4 NOVEMBER

5 NOVEMBER

6 NOVEMBER

7 NOVEMBER

8 NOVEMBER

9 NOVEMBER

10 NOVEMBER

11 NOVEMBER

12 NOVEMBER

13 NOVEMBER

14 NOVEMBER

15 NOVEMBER

16 NOVEMBER

17 NOVEMBER

18 NOVEMBER

19 NOVEMBER

20 NOVEMBER

21 NOVEMBER

22 NOVEMBER

23 NOVEMBER

24 NOVEMBER

NOVEMBER

25 NOVEMBER

26 NOVEMBER

27 NOVEMBER

28 NOVEMBER

29 NOVEMBER

30 NOVEMBER

DECEMBER

I knelt down and cautiously lifted the box lid a few inches. I peered into the darkness inside. There was a lot of soft straw. Huddled right in the middle, ears twitching anxiously, was a little grey rabbit.

COOKIE

1 DECEMBER

2 DECEMBER

3 DECEMBER

4 DECEMBER

5 DECEMBER

6 DECEMBER

7 DECEMBER

8 DECEMBER

9 DECEMBER

10 DECEMBER

11 DECEMBER

12 DECEMBER

13 DECEMBER

14 DECEMBER

15 DECEMBER

16 DECEMBER

17 DECEMBER

18 DECEMBER

19 DECEMBER

20 DECEMBER

21 DECEMBER

22 DECEMBER

23 DECEMBER

24 DECEMBER

25 DECEMBER

26 DECEMBER

27 DECEMBER

28 DECEMBER

29 DECEMBER

30 DECEMBER

31 DECEMBER

NOTES

HAVE YOU SEEN THIS OTHER GORGEOUS JACQUELINE WILSON STATIONERY?

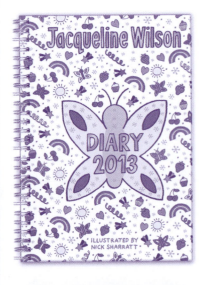

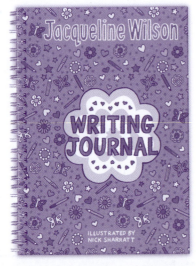

CHECK OUT JACQUELINE WILSON'S OFFICIAL WEBSITE!

You'll find lots of fun stuff including games and amazing competitions. You can even customise your own page and start an online diary!

You'll find out all about Jacqueline in her monthly diary and tour blogs, as well as seeing her replies to fan mail. You can also chat to other fans on the message boards.

Join in today at
www.jacquelinewilson.co.uk

And watch the brilliant video trailers for Jacqueline's books at
www.youtube.com/jacquelinewilson.tv